My First
Scripture
Journal

Visit us at DeseretBook.com

ISBN 978-1-60907-549-1

Printed in China   04/2016
RR Donnelley, Shenzhen, China

10   9   8   7   6

For my soul
delighteth in the scriptures,
and my heart pondereth them.
—2 Nephi 4:15

This journal will help you ponder and understand the Book of Mormon.

1. Find and read the scripture verse in your Book of Mormon.

2. Read the questions and think about what the verse means to you.

3. Write down your answers to the questions.

1 Nephi 1:5 Lehi prayed with his whole heart.

What do you think it means to pray with your whole heart?

_____

_____

_____

_____

When was a time you prayed with your whole heart?

_____

_____

_____

_____

_____

_____

1 Nephi 2:4 Lehi and his family left all their gold and silver behind when they went into the wilderness.

Why do you think they were willing to leave these things behind?

_____

_____

_____

_____

_____

If you had to leave your home, what would be the hardest thing for you to leave behind?

_____

_____

_____

_____

_____

1 Nephi 3:19-20 The words of the prophets were recorded on the brass plates.

Why do you think it would be good for Lehi's family to have the brass plates while they journeyed to the promised land?

_____

_____

_____

_____

_____

What is one way the scriptures or words of the prophets have helped you?

_____

_____

_____

_____

_____

_____

1 Nephi 4:6 Nephi was led, or guided, by the Spirit to do the things the Lord wanted him to do.

What do you think it means to be led by the Spirit?

_____

_____

_____

_____

Write about a time you felt the Holy Ghost guiding you to do something.

_____

_____

_____

_____

_____

_____

1 Nephi 4:33

Nephi made an oath, or a promise, to Zoram that if he would travel into the wilderness with Lehi's family, he would be a free man.

How you think Zoram felt when Nephi made this promise to him?

_____

_____

_____

_____

_____

How do you feel when you keep your promises?

_____

_____

_____

_____

_____

1 Nephi 5:14 Because of the brass plates, Lehi's family knew who their ancestors were.

Why do you think it's good for us to know who our ancestors were?

_____

_____

_____

_____

_____

Write the names of your parents and grandparents.

_____

_____

_____

_____

_____

_____

1 Nephi 8:37 Lehi loved his children and taught them the gospel.

Why do you think the Lord asks parents to teach their children the truth?

_____

_____

_____

_____

What have your parents taught you that shows they love you?

_____

_____

_____

_____

_____

1 Nephi 9:6 Nephi bore his testimony of God's knowledge and power.

How does it make you feel to know that God knows all things and has all power?

_____

_____

_____

_____

_____

Write your testimony about how Heavenly Father knows you and loves you.

_____

_____

_____

_____

_____

1 Nephi 10:5 All of the prophets bear testimony of the Messiah and Redeemer of the world, who is Jesus Christ.

Why do you think the prophets teach about Jesus Christ?

_____

_____

_____

_____

_____

Write what you have learned about why Jesus came to the earth.

_____

_____

_____

_____

_____

1 Nephi 15:34 Nephi taught that no unclean thing can enter the kingdom of God.

What do you think it means to be unclean?

_____

_____

_____

_____

_____

What can you do to keep your mind and body clean?

_____

_____

_____

_____

_____

_____

_____

1 Nephi 16:10 Lehi's family were given the Liahona to guide them on their journey.

Why do you think it would be good to have something like a Liahona to help you on a journey?

_____

_____

_____

_____

What do you have that can help to guide you in your life every day?

_____

_____

_____

_____

_____

1 Nephi 16:28 The pointers in the Liahona worked only when Lehi's family were faithful and obedient.

How do you think the Liahona is like the Holy Ghost?

_____

_____

_____

_____

_____

Tell about a time when you think the Holy Ghost was guiding you.

_____

_____

_____

_____

_____

1 Nephi 16:32 Lehi's family gave thanks to God for their food.

Why do you think it's important to thank God for our food—even if we bought it or grew it ourselves?

_____

_____

_____

_____

_____

Write down as many things as you can think of that you would like to thank God for.

_____

_____

_____

_____

_____

1 Nephi 17:15 Nephi wanted his brothers to pay attention to the word of God and to keep His commandments.

Why do you think Nephi wanted so much for his brothers to listen to and obey God?

_____

_____

_____

_____

_____

What is something that you know God wants you to be more faithful in doing?

_____

_____

_____

_____

_____

_____

1 Nephi 17:36 The Lord created the earth as a home for His children.

Why do you think the Lord wanted to create an earth for us to live on?

_____

_____

_____

_____

_____

What are some of your favorite things to see and do on this earth?

_____

_____

_____

_____

_____

1 Nephi 17:45 When Nephi's brothers chose to disobey God's commandments, it was hard for them to hear and feel the still, small voice of the Holy Ghost.

Why do you think it's hard to hear the Holy Ghost when we are not doing what is right?

_____

_____

_____

_____

_____

What are the good things you do that help you to hear the Holy Ghost?

_____

_____

_____

_____

_____

1 Nephi 18:16 Even though he had many troubles, Nephi praised the Lord and didn't complain.

Why do you think it's important not to complain but to try to be cheerful when things go wrong?

_____

_____

_____

_____

_____

Write about a time when you were tempted to complain but tried to smile instead.

_____

_____

_____

_____

_____

1 Nephi 19:1 After their arrival in the promised land, Nephi was instructed by the Lord to keep a record of his people.

Why do you think the Lord wanted Nephi to keep a record?

_____

_____

_____

_____

What kinds of things do you like to write about in your journal?

_____

_____

_____

_____

_____

_____

1 Nephi 19:18 Nephi kept his record in order to help his people to remember the Lord, their Redeemer.

Why do you think it was good for the people to remember the Lord?

_____

_____

_____

_____

_____

When you think about Jesus, what feelings do you have?

_____

_____

_____

_____

_____

_____

2 Nephi 1:30 Zoram was a true friend to Nephi.

What do you think it means to be a true friend?

_____

_____

_____

_____

Write about the things you do that show you are a true friend.

_____

_____

_____

_____

_____

2 Nephi 2:1 Jacob had suffered as a boy because of the rudeness of his brothers.

Why do you think people are rude sometimes?

_____

_____

_____

_____

_____

What things can you do to get along better with your family?

_____

_____

_____

_____

_____

_____

2 Nephi 2:25 Lehi taught that Heavenly Father wants us to have joy in this life.

What do you think it means to have joy?

_____

_____

_____

_____

Write down ten things that make you happy.

_____

_____

_____

_____

_____

_____

2 Nephi 4:15 Nephi read the scriptures to his family and taught that we can learn things from the scriptures that will help us in our lives.

What do you think it means to "delight in the scriptures"?

_____

_____

_____

_____

_____

What is something you have learned from the scriptures that helps you every day?

_____

_____

_____

_____

_____

_____

2 Nephi 4:16 Nephi loved to ponder the things of the Lord.

What do you think it means to "ponder" something?

_____

_____

_____

_____

When you think about, or ponder, the things you learn in Primary, how do you feel?

_____

_____

_____

_____

_____

_____

2 Nephi 5:16 Nephi built a temple.

Why do you think it was good for the people to have a temple?

_____

_____

_____

_____

_____

How do you feel when you see a temple or a picture of a temple?

_____

_____

_____

_____

_____

_____

_____

2 Nephi 9:52 Praying to God every day helps us to rejoice.

Why do you think that remembering to pray every day helps us to be happy?

_____

_____

_____

_____

Make a list of some things you can thank Heavenly Father for when you pray tonight.

_____

_____

_____

_____

_____

2 Nephi 10:23 Jacob taught that God wants us to make choices.

Why do you think it's important that we be able to choose?

_____

_____

_____

_____

What are some choices you have needed to make today?

_____

_____

_____

_____

_____

2 Nephi 22:5 Thinking about all of the "excellent" things the Lord has done sometimes makes us want to sing.

How many "excellent" things can you think of that the Lord has done?

_____

_____

_____

_____

_____

Write the words of one of your favorite Primary songs about Heavenly Father or Jesus.

_____

_____

_____

_____

_____

_____

2 Nephi 25:26 The prophet Nephi labored to persuade people to believe in Jesus Christ.

Why do you think Nephi wanted everyone to know about Jesus?

_____

_____

_____

_____

Who would you like to tell about Jesus Christ?

_____

_____

_____

_____

_____

2 Nephi 31:10 One of the best ways to follow Jesus is to keep the commandments.

What do you think it means to follow Jesus?

_____

_____

_____

_____

_____

Tell about something you did today that shows you are following Jesus.

_____

_____

_____

_____

_____

_____

2 Nephi 31:11 Heavenly Father wants us to repent and be baptized in Jesus' name.

Why do you think Heavenly Father wants us to be baptized?

_____

_____

_____

_____

Write about the feelings you had on your baptism day.

_____

_____

_____

_____

_____

2 Nephi 32:3 Nephi taught us to "feast upon the words of Christ."

What do you think it means to feast on Christ's words?

_____

_____

_____

_____

Write down a scripture you really like and make a plan to memorize it.

_____

_____

_____

_____

_____

2 Nephi 32:5 After we are baptized and are given the gift of the Holy Ghost, we can be guided by the Holy Ghost.

What do you think it feels like to have the Holy Ghost guide you?

_____

_____

_____

_____

Write about how you felt when you were given the gift of the Holy Ghost.

_____

_____

_____

_____

Jacob 7:10-11 Jacob and all other prophets
testify of Christ.

What do you think it means to testify?

_____

_____

_____

_____

_____

If you were a missionary, what would you tell people
about Jesus Christ?

_____

_____

_____

_____

_____

_____

Enos 1:4 Enos wanted God to know he was sorry for his sins, so he prayed all day and all night.

Why do you think Enos was able to pray for such a long time?

_____

_____

_____

_____

_____

What is something you would like to talk with God about?

_____

_____

_____

_____

_____

Enos 1:11 Enos prayed for the Lamanites, who were his enemies.

Why do you think God wants us to pray for those who are not kind to us?

_____

_____

_____

_____

_____

Have you ever prayed for someone who was not kind to you? Tell how that made you feel.

_____

_____

_____

_____

_____

Mosiah 2:6 The people gathered around the temple to hear the words of their king.

Why do you think the people thought it was so important to listen to their leader?

_____

_____

_____

_____

How do you feel when you hear our prophet speak to us today?

_____

_____

_____

_____

_____

Mosiah 2:17 King Benjamin taught his people that when they serve others, they are serving God at the same time.

Why do you think serving others is the same as serving the Lord?

_____

_____

_____

_____

_____

How do you feel inside when you help someone?

_____

_____

_____

_____

_____

_____

Mosiah 2:22 King Benjamin taught that when God's people obey His commandments, He blesses them and helps them prosper.

What do you think "prosper" means?

_____

_____

_____

_____

_____

What blessings have you received because you were obedient?

_____

_____

_____

_____

_____

Mosiah 2:41 When people obey God's commandments, they are happy.

Why do you think we are happy when we obey God?

_____

_____

_____

_____

_____

What do you think it will be like to live with God "in a state of neverending happiness"?

_____

_____

_____

_____

_____

_____

Mosiah 3:7 King Benjamin taught his people that Jesus Christ would suffer for us.

Why do you think Jesus was willing to suffer so much?

_____

_____

_____

_____

How can knowing this about Jesus help you when you are going through a hard time?

_____

_____

_____

_____

_____

Mosiah 3:20 Someday everyone in the world will learn about Jesus Christ.

How do you think all nations will learn about Jesus?

_____

_____

_____

_____

Write down one thing you can do to be a missionary now.

_____

_____

_____

_____

_____

_____

Mosiah 4:10 We need to repent of our sins and ask God to forgive us.

Why do you think it's sometimes hard to be humble and ask God for forgiveness?

_____

_____

_____

_____

_____

What is something you would like to ask God to forgive you for?

_____

_____

_____

_____

_____

Mosiah 4:14-15 Parents should love and teach their children.

What things do you think the Lord wants parents to teach their children?

_____

_____

_____

_____

_____

Name three things you do that show you are practicing what your parents have taught you.

_____

_____

_____

_____

_____

Mosiah 5:7 Because of their faith in Jesus Christ, King Benjamin's people made a covenant with God and became part of His family.

What do you think it means to make a covenant with God?

_____

_____

_____

_____

Knowing you have made a baptismal covenant and you belong to the family of Jesus Christ, how does this make you want to act each day?

_____

_____

_____

_____

Mosiah 5:15 If we always make good choices and do good things, we may live with God in heaven.

What do you think it means to be "steadfast and immovable"?

_____

_____

_____

_____

_____

What are some "good works" that you have done?

_____

_____

_____

_____

_____

_____

Mosiah 9:17 Zeniff's people prayed mightily and battled the Lamanites "in the strength of the Lord."

What do you think it means to do something in the strength of the Lord?

_____

_____

_____

_____

_____

Think of a situation in your life when you would need the strength and support of the Lord.

_____

_____

_____

_____

_____

Mosiah 10:4-5 Zeniff's people worked to build their city.

Why do you think it's important for us to work and take care of ourselves?

_____

_____

_____

_____

_____

Write down the things you are asked to do in your home to help your family.

_____

_____

_____

_____

_____

_____

Mosiah 11:23 If we turn to God and repent, we will not be brought into bondage.

What do you think it means to be in bondage to sin?

_____

_____

_____

_____

Write about how you think it would feel to be delivered from bondage.

_____

_____

_____

_____

_____

_____

Mosiah 13:20 One of the Ten Commandments that Abinadi recited to King Noah tells us to "honor thy father and thy mother."

What do you think it means to honor your parents?

_____

_____

_____

_____

_____

How do you show that you honor your parents?

_____

_____

_____

_____

_____

_____

_____

Mosiah 16:7-8 Because of Jesus, everyone will be resurrected.

Why do you think God wants all of His children to be resurrected?

_____

_____

_____

_____

_____

Why does it make you happy to know that everyone who dies will be resurrected?

_____

_____

_____

_____

_____

Mosiah 17:2 When the prophet Abinadi testified before wicked King Noah, Alma defended Abinadi.

Why do you think Alma was brave enough to plead with the king to let Abinadi go?

_____

_____

_____

_____

_____

Write about a time when you have stood up for someone or something that was good.

_____

_____

_____

_____

_____

Mosiah 17:8-9 Even though he would be put to death for what he had said about Jesus Christ and about the wickedness of King Noah and his priests, the prophet Abinadi would not take back his words.

Why do you think Abinadi would not deny what he had said?

_____

_____

_____

_____

_____

Write about a time when it wasn't easy for you to tell the truth.

_____

_____

_____

_____

_____

Mosiah 18:13-14 After their baptism, Alma and Helam were happy and were filled with the Spirit.

Why do you think the writer described baptism as being "buried in the water"?

_____

_____

_____

_____

_____

Describe the happy feelings you had when you were baptized.

_____

_____

_____

_____

_____

Mosiah 18:23 Alma taught his people to observe the Sabbath day.

Why do you think the Lord gave us the Sabbath day?

_____

_____

_____

_____

_____

What are some things you can do on Sunday that will help you observe the Sabbath day and keep it holy?

_____

_____

_____

_____

_____

_____

Mosiah 23:15 Alma taught his people to love each other and have no contention (or arguing).

What do you think it means that a person should "love his neighbor as himself"?

_____

_____

_____

_____

What can you do to help avoid contention, or angry disagreements, in your home?

_____

_____

_____

_____

_____

Mosiah 24:15 The Lord strengthened Alma's people so that their burdens were not so heavy.

How do you think Alma's people felt when the Lord strengthened them?

_____

_____

_____

_____

_____

What can you think about to help you be cheerful and patient when you are asked to do something hard?

_____

_____

_____

_____

_____

_____

Mosiah 27:14 Because he had faith, Alma's prayers for his rebellious son Alma were answered.

Why do you think Alma prayed so hard for his son?

_____

_____

_____

_____

_____

Think of someone who needs help that you could pray for.

_____

_____

_____

_____

_____

_____

_____

Mosiah 27:34-35 The four sons of King Mosiah repented of their sins.

What are some of the things the sons of Mosiah did as part of their repentance?

_____

_____

_____

_____

_____

Write about how you felt when you repented of something you had done wrong.

_____

_____

_____

_____

_____

_____

Mosiah 28:1 King Mosiah's sons wanted to serve as missionaries among the Lamanites.

Why do you think the sons of Mosiah were willing to teach the gospel to people who might not want to listen?

_____

_____

_____

_____

Write three things you can do to prepare to serve a mission.

_____

_____

_____

_____

_____

Mosiah 28:6-7 The Lord told Mosiah that his sons would have success and be protected.

How do you think King Mosiah felt to know the Lord would protect and help his sons?

_____

_____

_____

_____

_____

What kinds of things do you think your parents pray for when they talk to the Lord about you?

_____

_____

_____

_____

_____

_____

Alma 1:27 The people gave freely to the poor, and they dressed modestly.

How do you think it made the people feel when they helped those who were poor and needy?

_____

_____

_____

_____

_____

What kinds of things can you do to help those who don't have as much as you do?

_____

_____

_____

_____

_____

_____

Alma 4:10 Many Nephite church members were a bad example to those who did not belong to the church.

What do you think it means that the wickedness of the church members was a "stumbling-block" to other people?

_____

_____

_____

_____

_____

In what ways are you a good example of someone who belongs to the Lord's church?

_____

_____

_____

_____

_____

Alma 5:16 Alma asked the people to imagine what the Lord will say to them one day if they are righteous.

What do you think it will feel like to have the Lord tell you He is pleased with the choices you have made?

_____

_____

_____

_____

_____

What choices have you made today that you think the Lord would be pleased with?

_____

_____

_____

_____

_____

_____

Alma 5:47 Alma testified that the scriptures are true.

Why do you think it's important to know the scriptures are true?

_____

_____

_____

_____

_____

What can you do to find out for yourself that the scriptures are true?

_____

_____

_____

_____

_____

_____

Alma 5:48 Alma bore his testimony of Jesus Christ.

How do you feel when you hear someone tell stories or bear their testimony of Jesus?

_____

_____

_____

_____

_____

Write down your testimony about Jesus Christ.

_____

_____

_____

_____

_____

_____

Alma 7:11-12 Jesus Christ experienced pain, sickness, and temptation so that He would know how to help us.

Why do you think Jesus wants to help us in our troubles?

_____

_____

_____

_____

_____

Write about a time when you have been able to help someone else because you knew what they were feeling.

_____

_____

_____

_____

_____

Alma 10:7 Amulek was blessed for honoring a prophet.

How do you think Amulek felt when the angel told him he should help the prophet Alma?

_____

_____

_____

_____

What do you do to show that you respect God's prophet today?

_____

_____

_____

_____

_____

Alma 11:45 When we are resurrected, our bodies and spirits will be united forever.

What do you think we will look like after we are resurrected?

_____

_____

_____

_____

Write about how you will feel to see all of your family when you are all resurrected.

_____

_____

_____

_____

_____

Alma 17:2 Alma and the sons of Mosiah knew the scriptures were true because they had diligently studied the words of God.

What do you think it means to search the scriptures diligently?

_____

_____

_____

_____

Write down your favorite scripture or scripture story.

_____

_____

_____

_____

_____

Alma 17:10 The Lord comforted the sons of Mosiah through His Spirit.

Why do you think the Lord wanted to comfort His servants?

_____

_____

_____

_____

_____

Tell about a time when you felt the Holy Ghost giving you comfort.

_____

_____

_____

_____

_____

_____

Alma 21:23 The people listened to Ammon and wanted to keep God's commandments.

What do you think it means that the people "were zealous for keeping the commandments of God"?

_____

_____

_____

_____

_____

Tell about a time when you have been excited to do something your teacher or parent taught you about.

_____

_____

_____

_____

_____

Alma 24:19 The people of Ammon believed the truth so much that they buried their weapons of war.

Why do you think these Lamanites changed so much that they buried their weapons?

_____

_____

_____

_____

How are you willing to change so that you can show that you believe and know the truth?

_____

_____

_____

_____

_____

Alma 26:12 Ammon knew that God had helped them be successful missionaries to the Lamanites.

Why do you think Ammon didn't boast about what they had accomplished?

_____

_____

_____

_____

_____

Write about a time when you knew that God was helping you and how you felt.

_____

_____

_____

_____

_____

Alma 32:21 To have faith means that we believe in things that are true even though we can't see them.

Why do you think it's important to believe in God and His plan even if we can't see Him?

_____

_____

_____

_____

Write down some things you know are true about Heavenly Father and Jesus even though you haven't seen them.

_____

_____

_____

_____

_____

Alma 33:6 God hears our prayers.

Why do you think God wants us to pray to Him?

_____

_____

_____

_____

_____

Tell about a time when you knew that God heard your
prayer or a prayer of someone you know.

_____

_____

_____

_____

_____

_____

Alma 36:3 Alma taught his son Helaman that
if we trust God He will help us through our trials and
troubles.

How do you think God supports us in our trials?

_____

_____

_____

_____

Write about a time when you trusted in Heavenly Father
and felt Him helping you.

_____

_____

_____

_____

_____

Alma 37:37 Alma taught his son Helaman to "counsel with the Lord" in all his "doings."

What do you think it means to counsel with the Lord?

_____

_____

_____

_____

_____

Write about a time when you talked with Heavenly Father about something that was important to you.

_____

_____

_____

_____

_____

_____

Alma 37:44 Alma compared the words of Christ to the Liahona, the compass that pointed the way to the promised land.

How do you think the words of Christ are like a compass?

_____

_____

_____

_____

_____

Write about a time when something you learned about in the scriptures helped you make a good choice.

_____

_____

_____

_____

_____

Alma 38:2 Alma was glad that his son Shiblon had faith in God.

Why do you think it made Alma so happy that his son was true in keeping God's commandments?

_____

_____

_____

_____

Tell about some things that you do that bring your parents joy.

_____

_____

_____

_____

_____

Alma 41:10 Alma told his son Corianton that he could not be wicked and still be happy.

Why do you think we can't feel happy when we know we've made a bad choice?

_____

_____

_____

_____

Think of a time when you made a wrong choice and write about how that made you feel.

_____

_____

_____

_____

_____

Alma 45:15 Alma gave a blessing to each of his sons.

How do you think Alma's sons felt when their father gave them blessings?

_____

_____

_____

_____

Write about a time when your father or another priesthood holder gave you a blessing.

_____

_____

_____

_____

_____

_____

Alma 46:11-12 Captain Moroni made a flag to remind his people of the important things they needed to fight for.

Why do you think Captain Moroni thought it was important to fight for freedom and peace?

_____

_____

_____

_____

What things would you write on your own title of liberty (or flag)?

_____

_____

_____

_____

_____

Alma 48:11 Captain Moroni was courageous and good.

Why do you think the people wanted to follow Captain Moroni?

_____

_____

_____

_____

_____

Write about one of your heroes and the good qualities that person has.

_____

_____

_____

_____

_____

Alma 56:47 The 2,000 young warriors were taught by their mothers to put their faith in God.

Why do you think the young warriors were not afraid to fight?

_____

_____

_____

_____

_____

How have your parents or teachers taught you to have faith in your Heavenly Father?

_____

_____

_____

_____

_____

_____

Alma 57:21 The 2,000 young warriors obeyed every command with exactness.

What do you think it means to obey "with exactness"?

_____

_____

_____

_____

How can you do your work at home with exactness?

_____

_____

_____

_____

_____

_____

Alma 62:49 Even though some of the people were rich and powerful, they remembered God and were humble.

Why do you think it's important to always remember that we need God's help in our lives?

_____

_____

_____

_____

_____

What are some ways you can show you are humble?

_____

_____

_____

_____

_____

Helaman 5:6 Helaman taught his sons Nephi and Lehi to remember the special names they had been given.

How do you think it would help Helaman's sons to remember their ancestors?

_____

_____

_____

_____

_____

What things help you to remember that you are a child of God?

_____

_____

_____

_____

_____

Helaman 5:9 Helaman taught his sons that we should always remember Jesus.

Why do you think remembering what Jesus has done for you helps you in your life?

_____

_____

_____

_____

_____

What do you do that helps you to think of Jesus every day?

_____

_____

_____

_____

_____

Helaman 5:12 Helaman taught his sons that when we try to follow Jesus, it is like building a house on a strong rock.

How do you think Jesus is like a rock that we can build our lives on?

_____

_____

_____

_____

_____

What is one way you are building your life on Christ's teachings?

_____

_____

_____

_____

_____

Helaman 6:3 The members of the Church were glad when new people joined the Church.

What do you think it means to "fellowship" one another?

_____

_____

_____

_____

_____

How do you show that you are glad to be with your friends at church?

_____

_____

_____

_____

_____

_____

_____

Helaman 10:4 Nephi was diligent and
obedient in doing what the Lord wanted him to do.

What do you think it means that Nephi did God's work
"with unwearyingness"?

_____

_____

_____

_____

_____

How can you be diligent and do your work at home and
at school with unwearyingness?

_____

_____

_____

_____

_____

Helaman 14:2-3 The prophet Samuel the Lamanite told the Nephites about signs that would appear when Jesus was born.

Why do you think God wanted the Nephites to know of these signs?

_____

_____

_____

_____

_____

What can you do to be better prepared when Jesus comes to the earth again?

_____

_____

_____

_____

_____

_____

Helaman 14:17 Samuel the Lamanite taught that Jesus died and was resurrected to make it possible for us to return to Heavenly Father.

How does it make you feel to know that you can return to live with Heavenly Father and Jesus?

_____

_____

_____

_____

_____

What choices did you make today that will help you return to live with Heavenly Father?

_____

_____

_____

_____

_____

3 Nephi 5:12-13 The prophet Mormon was a disciple of Christ who was called by God to teach the gospel to his people.

What do you think it means to be a disciple of Christ?

_____

_____

_____

_____

_____

Tell about something you do that shows you are a disciple of Christ.

_____

_____

_____

_____

_____

3 Nephi 9:14 The Lord wants everyone to come to Him and have eternal life.

Why do you think the Lord opens His arms to everyone?

_____

_____

_____

_____

_____

Write about how you think it will feel to have the Lord's arms around you.

_____

_____

_____

_____

_____

3 Nephi 11:24-26 Jesus taught the Nephites the proper way to baptize.

Why do you think it's important to be baptized in the way Jesus taught?

_____

_____

_____

_____

_____

Write about the priesthood holder who baptized you and tell why he is special to you.

_____

_____

_____

_____

_____

3 Nephi 11:30 Jesus taught that He does not want us to be angry with each other.

Why do you think people are sometimes stirred up to anger?

_____

_____

_____

_____

When you are angry, how can you remember to follow Jesus?

_____

_____

_____

_____

_____

3 Nephi 12:9 Those who are peacemakers act like they are God's children.

What do you think it means to be a peacemaker?

_____

_____

_____

_____

_____

How can you be a peacemaker in your home?

_____

_____

_____

_____

_____

_____

3 Nephi 12:16 When we let our light shine and do good things, we help Heavenly Father's work.

What do you think it means to let your light shine?

_____

_____

_____

_____

_____

In what ways are you a good example to people who know you?

_____

_____

_____

_____

_____

_____

3 Nephi 12:48 Jesus wants us to become perfect, just as He and Heavenly Father are perfect.

What do you think Jesus means when He asks us to become perfect?

_____

_____

_____

_____

Write down one way you would like to be like Heavenly Father and Jesus and what you will do today to help you reach that goal.

_____

_____

_____

_____

_____

3 Nephi 14:12 We need to treat other people the way we would want to be treated.

Why do you think it's important to be kind to others?

_____

_____

_____

_____

_____

Tell about a time when you chose to be kind to someone who had hurt your feelings.

_____

_____

_____

_____

_____

_____

3 Nephi 17:21 Jesus blessed the Nephite children and prayed for them.

How do you think the Nephite people felt when Jesus blessed the children?

_____

_____

_____

_____

Imagine how it would feel to see Jesus, and write down your feelings.

_____

_____

_____

_____

_____

3 Nephi 18:21 Jesus instructed the Nephites to pray with their families.

Why do you think the Lord wants us to have family prayer?

_____

_____

_____

_____

_____

What can you do to encourage your family to have prayer together?

_____

_____

_____

_____

_____

3 Nephi 24:10 Jesus reminded the Nephites of the commandment to pay tithing.

Why do you think the Lord asks us to pay tithing?

_____

_____

_____

_____

How do you feel when you know you are obeying the Lord when you pay your tithing?

_____

_____

_____

_____

_____

_____

3 Nephi 27:7 Jesus said that His church should be called by His name.

Why do you think Jesus wants His church to be called by His own name?

_____

_____

_____

_____

_____

How does it make you feel to belong to Jesus' church?

_____

_____

_____

_____

_____

_____

Ether 3:12 God always speaks the truth and never lies.

How does it make you feel to know that God always tells the truth?

_____

_____

_____

_____

_____

List some of the promises the Lord has made to you.

_____

_____

_____

_____

_____

_____

_____

Ether 6:3 The Lord gave the Jaredites light so they wouldn't cross the waters in darkness.

Why do you think the Lord wanted His people to have light on their journey?

_____

_____

_____

_____

_____

How are the scriptures like a light to you in your life?

_____

_____

_____

_____

_____

_____

Ether 12:27 The Lord will help us overcome our weaknesses.

Why do you think it's important to be humble and ask God to help us to be better people?

_____

_____

_____

_____

_____

Write down something you would like to ask God to help you with.

_____

_____

_____

_____

_____

_____

Ether 12:41 The prophet Moroni told us that we should "seek Jesus."

What do you think it means to seek Jesus?

_____

_____

_____

_____

_____

What have you done today to come closer to Jesus?

_____

_____

_____

_____

_____

_____

Moroni 4:3 The prophet Moroni recorded the prayer used to bless the sacrament bread.

How do you think the sacrament bread helps us remember Jesus?

_____

_____

_____

_____

How do you show that you are willing to keep the Lord's commandments?

_____

_____

_____

_____

_____

Moroni 5:2 Moroni also recorded the prayer used to bless the sacrament water or wine.

How do you think the sacrament water helps us remember Jesus?

_____

_____

_____

_____

_____

How do you show that you remember Jesus every day?

_____

_____

_____

_____

_____

_____

_____

Moroni 7:12-13 Evil comes from Satan, and good things come from God.

How do you feel when you are tempted to do something wrong—and how do you feel when you have an idea to do something good?

_____

_____

_____

_____

Tell about a time when you had to make a choice between wrong and right, and how you felt after you made your choice.

_____

_____

_____

_____

_____

Moroni 7:37 Mormon taught that miracles are possible when we have faith in Jesus Christ.

If you had to explain what a miracle is to someone, what would you tell them?

_____

_____

_____

_____

_____

Write about a miracle that has happened to you or someone you know, or find an example in the scriptures or Church history.

_____

_____

_____

_____

_____

Moroni 7:47 The prophet Mormon taught us that we need to have charity, which is the pure love of Christ.

What do you think it means to have the pure love of Christ?

_____

_____

_____

_____

Tell how you would treat people if you loved them like Jesus does.

_____

_____

_____

_____

_____

Moroni 10:4 The Holy Ghost can help us know the Book of Mormon is true.

Why do you think God wants us to know the Book of Mormon is true?

_____

_____

_____

_____

_____

Tell how you know you are feeling the Holy Ghost when you read the Book of Mormon.

_____

_____

_____

_____

_____

Moroni 10:5 The Holy Ghost can teach us the truth about all things.

How do you think the Holy Ghost helps us know the truth?

_____

_____

_____

_____

_____

What can you do to help the Holy Ghost teach you?

_____

_____

_____

_____

_____

_____